Honestly, RED RIDING HOOD WAS ROTTEN!

The story of LITTLE RED RIDING HOOD

as told by THE WOLF

by Trisha Shaskan

illustrated by Gerald Guerlais

raintree

a Capstone company — publishers for children

Raintree is an imprint of Capstone Global Library Limited,
a company incorporated in England and Wales having its
registered office at 264 Banbury Road, Oxford, OX2 7DY –
Registered company number: 6695582

www.raintree.co.uk
myorders@raintree.co.uk

We would like to thank Terry Flaherty, Professor of
English at Minnesota State University, for his advice
and expertise.

Editors: Jill Kalz and Vaarunika Dharmapala
Designer: Lori Bye
Art Director: Nathan Gassman
Production Specialist: Sarah Bennett
The illustrations in this book were created digitally.

ISBN 978 1 406 24310 9 (paperback)
16 15 14 13 12
10 9 8 7 6 5 4 3 2 1

British Library Cataloguing in Publication Data
A full catalogue record for this book is available from
the British Library.

Printed and Bound in the United Kingdom

Chomp! Chomp! Oh, I'm sorry. I was just finishing my lunch. My name's Wolf – Big Bad Wolf. You may have heard the story of Little Red Riding Hood. It's about a girl and her granny? Seems everyone has. My tail is different. Did I say *tail*? I meant *tale*.

Once upon a time, I ran out of food. Completely. The cupboards were bare. The freezer, too. I'd even eaten every last fruit and vegetable in the garden. **Every one**.

Other wolves might've lunched on little forest creatures: hedgehogs, bunnies, squirrels. I, however, am a vegetarian. That's right; I don't eat meat. Well, I *try* not to. I **LOVE** apples. Red Pippins, Cox's Orange Pippins, Bramleys ... Any kind, really. Sadly, there was still a long time to go until apple season.

I hadn't eaten in weeks. My stomach growled and howled. It moaned and groaned. It even roared. Then, my nose took over.

Sniff. Sniff. I took a whiff. What was it?

A girl.

Sniff. Sniff. I took a whiff. What was it?

Cake. Butter. In *this* forest? I had to investigate.

4

Suddenly, there she was: Little Red Riding Hood.
She looked as plump and juicy as a big, sweet APPLE.

Little Red twitched her cape. "Isn't it pretty?"
she asked.

"Certainly," I said.

"Aren't I pretty?" she asked.

Was she admiring herself in that puddle?

6

"With this cape," she said, "I'm even prettier than usual."

Gosh, she really was full of herself. My stomach growled.

Little Red twirled a strand of hair around her finger.
"Mother says the cape looks grand with my skin.
My skin shines likes pearls."

Or the flesh of a ripe apple, I thought, licking
my chops.

Remember, I hadn't eaten in weeks.
Time to chomp!

Then Little Red said, "I can't wait until Granny sees
how pretty I am today. I'm taking her cake and butter
from my mother."

My stomach howled. TWO meals, I thought: Granny
for breakfast and Little Red for lunch, with cake and
butter for dessert.

"Where does Granny live?" I asked.

Little Red pointed. "Down there, in the clearing.
The little brown house."

I knew that house. I had a plan!

"Let's play a game," I said.

Little Red smiled. "I'm really good at games."

"I'm sure you are," I said. "You take this path and I'll take that path. Let's see who arrives at Granny's first."

"I will," she said. "I'm the prettiest *and* the fastest."

"I'm sure you are," I said.

My stomach moaned. Before it groaned, I ran. No one knows the forest the way I do. I had chosen the shorter path.

THIS PATH

THAT PATH

Sniff. Sniff. I took a whiff. What was it?

Apple air freshener?

Tap, tap. I knocked on the door.

"Who's there?" called out a voice.

"Your granddaughter," I squeaked. "I've brought you cake and butter from Mother."

"Door's open," Granny said.

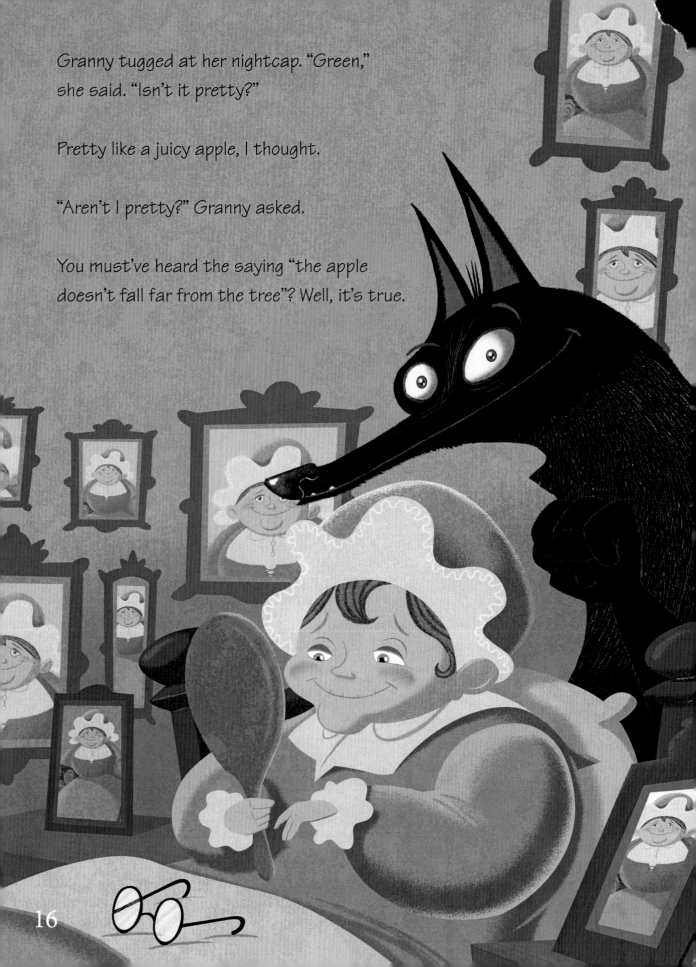

Granny tugged at her nightcap. "Green," she said. "Isn't it pretty?"

Pretty like a juicy apple, I thought.

"Aren't I pretty?" Granny asked.

You must've heard the saying "the apple doesn't fall far from the tree"? Well, it's true.

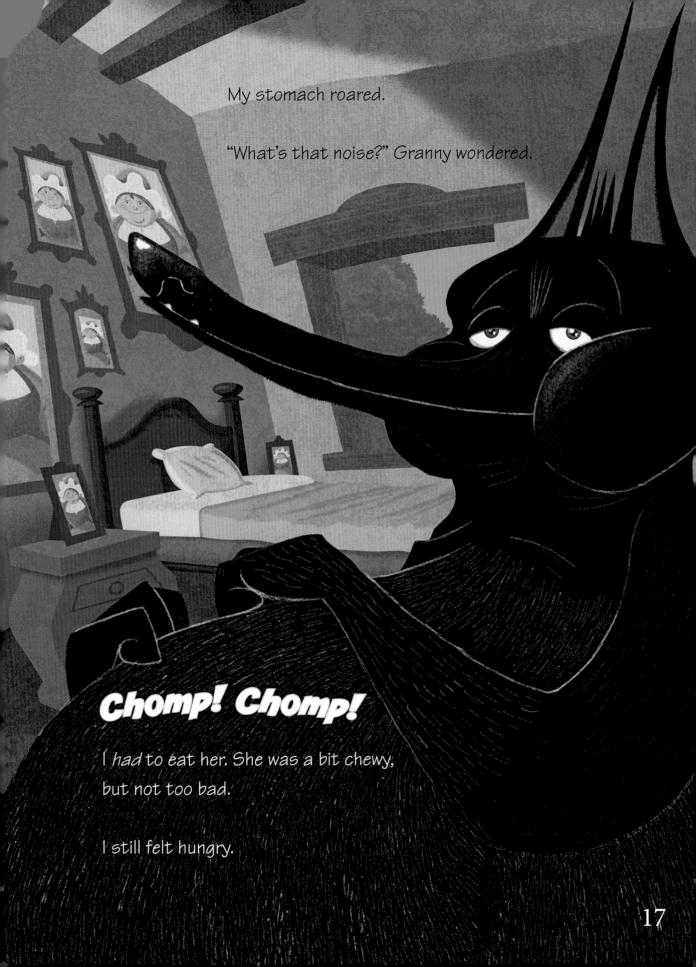

My stomach roared.

"What's that noise?" Granny wondered.

Chomp! Chomp!

I *had* to eat her. She was a bit chewy, but not too bad.

I still felt hungry.

Tap, tap. Little Red knocked on the door.

"Who's there?" I called out, crawling into Granny's bed.

"Your granddaughter," Little Red said. "I've brought you cake and butter from Mother."

"Door's open," I said.

Little Red walked in and caught a glimpse of herself in the mirror. "Isn't my cape pretty, Granny?" she said. "Aren't I pretty?"

I clenched my teeth.

"Granny," Little Red said,
"what deep dark eyes I have."

"Mmmhmm," I said,
"the colour of apple seed

"Granny," she said,
"what perfect ears I have."

"Mmmhmm," I said,
"shaped like apple slices."

"**Granny,**" she said,
"**what pretty red lips I have.**"

"**Mmmhmm,**" I said, "**deliciously red.**"

"**Granny,**" she said,
"**what lovely
skin I have.**"

Chomp! Chomp!

I ate her up. What can I say? Things look different when you're hungry. She wasn't sweet and crunchy (in fact, she was a bit rotten), but she was better than nothing.

Then, I had dessert.

Think about it

Read a classic version of *Little Red Riding Hood*. Now look at the Big Bad Wolf's version of the story. List some things that happened in the classic version that did not happen in Wolf's version. Then list some things that happened in Wolf's version that did not happen in the classic. How are the two versions different?

If it had been apple season, do you think Wolf would have eaten Little Red and Granny? Why or why not?

The classic version of *Little Red Riding Hood* is told from an invisible narrator's point of view. Wolf's story is from his point of view. Which point of view do you think is true?

How would other fairy tales change if they were told from another point of view? For example, how would Cinderella's story change if one of her stepsisters was the narrator? What if Baby Bear in *Goldilocks and the Three Bears* told that story? Write your own version of a classic fairy tale from a new point of view.

ϡϢϣϤϥ

Glossary

character *person, animal, or creature in a story*

narrator *person who tells a story*

point of view *way of looking at something*

version *account of something from a certain point of view*

Books in this series:

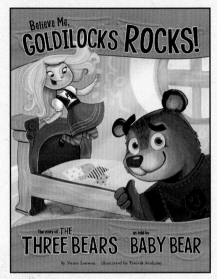

978 1 406 24309 3

978 1 406 24310 9

978 1 406 24311 6

978 1 406 24312 3